JACK and JILL

AND OTHER NURSERY RHYMES

Illustrated by Anne Sellers Leaf

Published by

THE TOON STUDIO
OF BEVERLY HILLS

JACK AND JILL

Jack and Jill went up the hill
To fetch a pail of water;
Jack fell down, and broke his crown,
And Jill came tumbling after.

Then up Jack got and off did trot
As fast as he could caper,
To old Dame Dob, who patched his nob
With vinegar and brown paper.

HARK, HARK!

Hark, hark! the dogs do bark!
Beggars are coming to town:
Some in jags, and some in rags,
And some in velvet gown.

CROSSPATCH

Crosspatch, draw the latch,
Sit by the fire and spin;
Take a cup and drink it up,
Then call your neighbors in.

PUSSYCAT BY THE FIRE

Pussycat sits by the fire;
How can she be fair?
In walks the little dog;
Says, "Pussy, are you there?
How do you do, Mistress Pussy?
Mistress Pussy, how d'ye do?"
"I thank you kindly, little dog,
I fare as well as you!"

A WEEK OF BIRTHDAYS

Monday's child is fair of face,
Tuesday's child is full of grace,
Wednesday's child is full of woe,
Thursday's child has far to go,
Friday's child is loving and giving
Saturday's child works hard for its living;
But the child that is born on the Sabbath day
Is bonny and blithe, and good and gay.

THE HOBBYHORSE

I had a little hobbyhorse,
And it was dapple gray;
Its head was made of pea-straw,
Its tail was made of hay.

I sold it to an old woman
For a copper groat;
And I'll not sing my song again
Without another coat.

GOING TO ST. IVES

As I was going to St. Ives
I met a man with seven wives.
Every wife had seven sacks,
Every sack had seven cats,
Every cat had seven kits.
Kits, cats, sacks, and wives,
How many were going to St. Ives?

THE WOMAN OF EXETER

There dwelt an old woman at Exeter;
When visitors came it sore vexed here,
So for fear they should eat,
She locked up all her meat,
This stingy old woman of Exeter.

THE KING OF FRANCE

The King of France went up the hill,
With twenty thousand men;
The King of France came down the hill,
And ne'er went up again.

WHAT ARE LITTLE BOYS MADE OF?

What are little boys made of, made of?
What are little boys made of?
"Snaps and sails, and puppy-dogs' tails;
And that's what little boys are made of."

What are little girls made of, made of?
What are little girls made of?
"Sugar and spice, and all that's nice;
And that's what little girls are made of."

GOOD KING ARTHUR

When good King Arthur ruled this land,
He was a goodly King;
He stole three pecks of barley meal,
To make a bag-pudding.
A bag-pudding the King did make,
And stuffed it well with plums,
And in it put great lumps of fat,
As big as my two thumbs.
The King and Queen did eat thereof,
And noblemen beside;
And what they could not eat that night,
The Queen next morning fried.

THE BOY AND THE SPARROW

A little cock-sparrow sat on a green tree,
And he chirruped, he chirruped, so merry was he;
A naughty boy came with his wee bow and arrow,
Determined to shoot this little cock-sparrow.

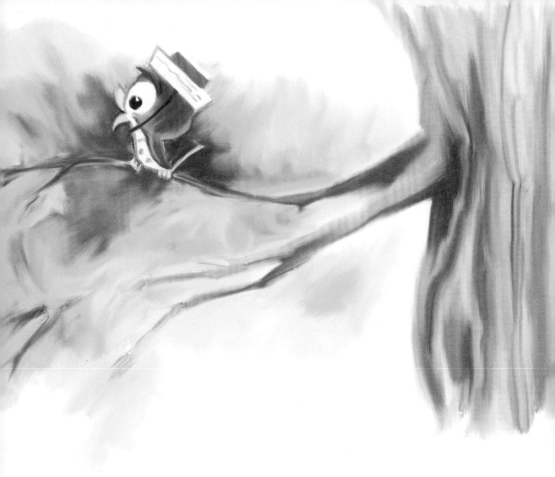

"This little cock-sparrow shall make me a stew,
And his giblets shall make me a little pie, too."
"Oh, no," says the sparrow, "I won't make a stew."
So he flapped his wings and away he flew.

THE LION AND THE UNICORN

The Lion and the Unicorn
were fighting for the crown,
The Lion beat the Unicorn
all around the town.
Some gave them white bread,
and some gave them brown,
Some gave them plumcake,
and sent them out of town.

PUSSYCAT AND QUEEN

"Pussycat, pussycat,
Where have you been?"
"I've been to London
To look at the Queen."

Pussycat, pussycat,
What did you there?"
"I frightened a little mouse
Under the chair."